# Angels Day Book

# ANGELS DAY BOOK

*A dateless diary in a timeless theme*

PEONY PRESS

This edition is published by Peony Press, an imprint of Anness Publishing Ltd, Hermes House, 88–89 Blackfriars Road, London SE1 8HA; tel. 020 7401 2077; fax 020 7633 9499
www.peonypress.com; www.annesspublishing.com

Anness Publishing has a new picture agency outlet for images for publishing, promotions or advertising. Please visit our website www.practicalpictures.com for more information.

Publisher: Joanna Lorenz
Editorial Manager: Joanne Rippin
Designer: Andrew Heath

ETHICAL TRADING POLICY
Because of our ongoing ecological investment programme, you, as our customer, can have the pleasure and reassurance of knowing that a tree is being cultivated on your behalf to naturally replace the materials used to make the book you are holding. For further information about this scheme, go to www.annesspublishing.com/trees



A CIP catalogue record for this book is available from the British Library

# Important Dates

## January

## February

## March

## April

## May

## June

## July

## August

## September

## October

## November

## December

THERE are two angels, that attend unseen
Each one of us, and in great books record
Our good and evil deeds. He who writes down
The good ones, after every action closes
His volume, and ascends with it to God.
The other keeps his dreadful day-book open
Till sunset, that we may repent; which doing,
The record of the action fades away,
And leaves a line of white across the page.

HENRY WADSWORTH LONGFELLOW *Christus*

1

2

3

4

5

6

7

He gave th' irrevocable sign,
Which mark'd to man the
hate divine;
And sudden from the
starting sky
The Angels of his wrath
bid fly!

MRS HANNAH COWLEDY

*Invocation to Horror*

8

9

10

11

12

13

14

15

16

17

18

19

20

21

22

23

Now like a mighty wind
they raise to heaven the
voice of song
Or like harmonious
thundering the seats of
heaven among
Beneath them sit the aged
men wise guardians
of the poor
Then cherish pity, lest you
drive an angel from
your door

WILLIAM BLAKE
*Holy Thursday*

24

25

26

27

28

29

30

31

I dreamt a dream! What can it mean?
And that I was a maiden Queen
Guarded by an Angel mild:
Witless woe was ne'er beguiled!

And I wept both night and day,
And he wiped my tears away;
And I wept both day and night,
And hid from him my heart's delight.

So he took his wings and fled;
Then the morn blushed rosy red.
I dried my tears, and armed my fears
With ten thousand shields and spears.

Soon my Angel came again;
I was armed, he came in vain;
For the time of youth was fled,
And grey hairs were on my head.

WILLIAM BLAKE *The Angel*

# FEBRUARY

1

2

3

4

5

6

7

8

9

10

11

12

13

14

And now 'twas like all
instruments,
Now like a lonely flute;
And now it is an
angel's song
That makes the heavens
be mute.

SAMUEL TAYLOR
COLERIDGE

*The Rime of the Ancyent
Mariner
in Seven Parts*

# FEBRUARY

15

16

17

18

19

20

21

22

23

24

25

26

27

28

29

And suddenly there was with the angel a multitude of the heavenly host praising God.

*The Gospel according to St Luke, Chapter 2, v. 13*

ABOU ben Adhem (may his tribe increase)
Awoke one night from a deep dream of peace,
And saw, within the moonlight in his room,
Making it rich, and like a lily in bloom,
An angel, writing in a book of gold: –
Exceeding peace had made Ben Adhem bold,
And to the presence in the room he said,
'What writest thou?' – The vision raised its head,
And, with a look made of all sweet accord,
Answered, 'The names of those who love the Lord.'
'And is mine one?' said Abou. 'Nay, not so,'
Replied the angel. Abou spoke more low,
But cheerly still; and said, 'I pray thee, then,
Write me as one that loves his fellow-men.'

The angel wrote, and vanished. The next night
It came again with a great wakening light,
And showed the names whom love of God had blessed,
And lo! Ben Adhem's name led all the rest.

LEIGH HUNT *Abou ben Adhem and the Angel*

# MARCH

1

2

3

4

5

From God our
heavenly Father
A blessed angel came,
And unto certain shepherds
Brought tiding of the same,
How that in Bethlehem
was born
The Son of God by name.

*God Rest You Merry Gentlemen*

6

7

8

9

10

11

12

13

14

15

16

17

18

For angels bright down
to me light:
Thou knowest
'tis no nay:
And for that sight thou
may'st delight
To sing, by by, lullay.

*This Endris Night*

19

20

21

22

23

24

25

26

27

28

29

30

31

A poor – torn heart – a tattered heart –
That sat it down to rest –
Nor noticed that the Ebbing Day
Flowed silver to the West –
Nor noticed Night did soft descend –
Nor Constellation burn –
Intent upon the vision
Of latitudes unknown.

The angels – happening that way
This dusty heart espied –
Tenderly took it up from toil
And carried it to God –
There – sandals for the Barefoot –
There – gathered from the gales –
Do the blue havens by the hand
Lead the wandering Sails.

EMILY DICKINSON No. 78 *A Poor, Torn Heart*

# APRIL

1

2

3

4

5

6

7

8

The angels all did sing
Praises to the heavenly
King

*Remember*

9

10

11

12

13

14

# APRIL

15

19

16

20

> As we watched at
> dead of night,
> Lo, we saw a wondrous light,
> Angels singing
> 'Peace on earth'
> Told us of the Saviour's
> birth.
>
> E. CASWALL
>
> *See Amid the Winter Snow*

21

26

22

27

23

28

17

24

29

18

25

30

ANGELS, from the realms of glory,
Wing your flight o'er all the earth;
Ye who sang creation's story
Now proclaim Messiah's birth:
Come and worship,
Worship Christ, the new-born King.

J MONTGOMERY *Angels, from the Realms of Glory*

# MAY

1

2

3

> That it may please Thee
> that after our death
> the Angels
> may carry our souls into
> Thy rest.
>
> *A Book of Litanies*

4

5

6

7

8

9

10

11

12

13

14

15

16

17

18

19

20

21

22

23

Made glad by the spiritual
gifts you offer
we sing with angels
the song of victory.
Alleluia!

*Liturgy for the Eucharistic Celebration, 3rd – 4th century*

24

25

26

27

28

29

30

31

AND in the sixth month the angel Gabriel was sent from God unto a city of Galilee, named Nazareth, to a virgin espoused to a man whose name was Joseph, of the house of David; and the virgin's name was Mary. And the angel came in unto her, and said, 'Hail, thou that art highly favoured, thc Lord is with thee: blessed art thou among women.' And when she saw him, she was troubled at his saying, and cast in her mind what manner of salutation this should be. And the angel said unto her, 'Fear not, Mary: for thou hast found favour with God. And, behold, thou shalt conceive in thy womb, and bring forth a son, and shalt call his name Jesus. He shall be great, and shall be called the Son of the Highest: and the Lord God shall give unto him the throne of his father David; and he shall reign over the house of Jacob for ever; and of his kingdom there shall be no end.'

*The Gospel according to Saint Luke, Ch1 v:26–33*

# JUNE

1

2

3

4

5

6

7

8

9

10

> The powers of heaven
> will be shaken;
> all the angels and archangels,
> the cherubim and seraphim
> will appear in fear and
> trembling before your glory.
>
> EPHREM SYRUS
> *Songs of Nisibis (1)*

11

12

13

14

15

# JUNE

16

17

18

19

20

21

22

23

24

25

26

27

And an angel of the Lord came up from Gilgal to Bochim, and said, I made you to go up out of Egypt, and have brought you unto the land which I sware unto your fathers.

*The Book of Judges, Chapter 2, v. 1*

28

29

30

IF the Celestials daily fly
With messages on missions high,
And float, our nests and turrets nigh,
  Conversing on Heaven's great intents;
What wonder hints of coming things,
Whereto men's hope and yearning clings,
Should drop like feathers from their wings
  And give us vague presentiments.

JEAN INGELOW from *Scholar and Carpenter*

ENOUGH for him, whom cherubim
Worship night and day,
A breastful of milk,
And a mangerful of hay;
Enough for him, whom angels
Fall down before,
The ox and ass and camel
Which adore.

Angels and archangels
May have gathered there,
Cherubim and seraphim
Thronged the air:
But only his mother
In her maiden bliss
Worshipped the Belovèd
With a kiss.

CHRISTINA ROSSETTI
*In the Bleak Mid-Winter*

# July

1

2

And he rode upon a cherub, and did fly: And he was seen upon the wings of the wind.

*The Second Book of Samuel, Chapter 22, v. 11*

3

4

5

6

7

8

9

10

11

12

13

14

15

16

21

22

23

17

24

18

25

19

26

20

27

28

29

But the angel of the Lord said to Elijah the Tishbite, Arise, go up to meet the messengers of the king of Samaria.

*The Second Book of Kings, Chapter 1, v. 3*

30

31

LITTLE Jesus, was Thou shy
Once, and just so small as I?
And what did it feel like to be
Out of Heaven, and just like me?
Didst Thou sometimes think of *there*,
And ask where all the angels were?
I should think that I would cry
For my house all made of sky;
I would look about the air,
And wonder where my angels were;
And at waking 'twould distress me –
Not an angel there to dress me!

Hadst Thou ever any toys,
Like us little girls and boys?
And didst Thou play in Heaven with all
The angels, that were not too tall,
With stars for marbles? Did the things
Play 'Can you see me?' through their wings?

FRANCIS THOMPSON *Ex Ore Infantium*

1

2

3

4

5

Then the angel of the Lord commanded Gad to say to David, that David should go up, and set up an altar unto the Lord.

*The First Book of Chronicles, Chapter 21, v. 18*

6

7

8

9

10

11

12

13

14

15

16

17

18

> And the Lord sent an angel, which cut off all the mighty men of valour, and the leaders and captains in the camp of the king of Assyria.
>
> *The Second Book of Chronicles, Chapter 32, v. 21*

19

20

21

22

23

24

25

26

27

28

29

30

31

AND their bright squadrons round
about us plant;
And all for love and nothing for reward:

EDMUND SPENSER *The Ministry of Angels*

# September

1

8

12

2

9

13

3

Then the angel of the Lord went forth, and smote in the camp of the Assyrians a hundred and fourscore and five thousand: and when they arose early in the morning, behold, they were all dead corpses.

*The Book of Isaiah, Chapter 37, v. 36*

14

4

15

5

6

10

7

11

16

17

18

19

20

21

22

23

24

25

26

27

28

29

30

Then I looked, and behold, in the firmament that was above the head of the cherubim there appeared over them as it were a sapphire stone, as the appearance of the likeness of a throne.

*The Book of Ezekiel, Chapter 10, v. 1*

AND is there care in Heaven? And is there love
In heavenly spirits to these creatures base,
That may compassion of their evils move?
There is: – else much more wretched were the case
Of men than beasts: but O! th'exceeding grace
Of highest God, that loves his creatures so,
And all his works with mercy doth embrace,
That blessed angels he sends to and fro,
To serve to wicked man, to serve his foe!

How oft do they their silver bowers leave
To come to succour us that succour want!
How oft do they with golden pinions cleave
The flitting skies, like flying pursuivant,
Against foul fiends to aid us militant!
They for us fight, they watch and duly ward,
And their bright squadrons round about us plant;
And all for love and nothing for reward:
O, why should heavenly God to men have such regard?

EDMUND SPENSER *The Ministry of Angels*

# OCTOBER

1

2

Behold, the angel of the Lord appeared unto him in a dream, saying, Joseph, thou son of David, fear not to take unto thee Mary thy wife.

*The Gospel according to St Matthew, Chapter 1, v. 20*

3

4

5

6

7

8

9

10

11

12

13

14

15

16

17

18

19

20

21

22

23

24

25

26

27

28

29

30

31

Behold, an angel of the Lord appeareth in a dream to Joseph in Egypt, saying, Arise, and take the young child and his mother, and go into the land of Israel

*The Gospel according to St Matthew, Chapter 2, vv. 19–20*

AND there was war in heaven: Michael and his angels fought against the dragon; and the dragon fought and his angels, and prevailed not; neither was their place found any more in heaven. And the great dragon was cast out, that old serpent, called the Devil, and Satan, which deceiveth the whole world: he was cast out into the earth, and his angels were cast out with him.

AND I saw an angel come down from heaven, having the key of the bottomless pit and a great chain in his hand. And he laid hold on the dragon, that old serpent, which is the Devil, and Satan, and bound him a thousand years, and cast him into the bottomless pit, and shut him up, and set a seal upon him, that he should deceive the nations no more, till the thousand years should be fulfilled: and after that he must be loosed a little season.

*The Revelation of St John the Divine, ch 12 v: 7–9 and ch 20 v: 1–2*

# NOVEMBER

1

2

3

4

5

6

7

8

9

10

11

12

13

14

15

And I saw another mighty angel come down from heaven, clothed with a cloud: and a rainbow was upon his head, and his face was as it were the sun, and his feet as pillars of fire.

*The Book of Revelation, Chapter 10, v. 1*

16

17

18

19

20

21

22

23

24

25

26

27

I saw four angels standing on the four corners of the earth, holding the four winds of the earth

*The Book of Revelation, Chapter 7, v. 1*

28

29

30

ON a starred night Prince Lucifer uprose.
Tired of his dark dominion swung the fiend
Above the rolling ball in cloud part screened,
Where sinners hugged their spectre of repose.
Poor prey to his hot fit of pride were those.
And now upon his western wing he leaned,
Now his huge bulk o'er Afric's sands careened,
Now the black planet shadowed Arctic snows.
Soaring through wider zones that pricked his scars
With memory of the old revolt from Awe,
He reached a middle height, and at the stars,
Which are the brain of heaven, he looked, and sank.
Around the ancient track marched, rank on rank,
The army of unalterable law.

GEORGE MEREDITH *Lucifer in Starlight*

# DECEMBER

1

2

3

4

5

6

7

8

9

10

11

12

13

14

15

And I saw the seven angels which stood before God; and to them were given seven trumpets.

*The Book of Revelation, Chapter 8, v. 2*

# DECEMBER

16

17

> And I saw another angel fly in the midst of heaven, having the everlasting gospel to preach unto them that dwell on the earth
>
> *The Book of Revelation, Chapter 14, v. 6*

18

19

20

21

22

23

24

25

26

27

28

29

30

31

Now when fair morn orient in heav'n appeared,
Up rose the victor Angels, and to arms
The matin trumpet sung: in arms they stood
Of golden panoply, refulgent host,
Soon banded: others from the dawning hills
Looked round, and scouts each coast light-armèd scour
Each quarter, to descry the distant foe,
Where lodged, or whither fled, or if for fight,
In motion or in halt: him soon they met,
Under spread ensigns moving nigh, in slow
But firm battalion: back with speediest sail
Zophiel, of Cherubim the swiftest wing,
Came flying, and in mid air aloud thus cried:
'Arm, warriors, arm for fight! the foe at hand,
Whom fled we thought, will save us long pursuit
This day; fear not his flight; so thick a cloud
He comes, and settled in his face I see
Sad resolution and secure: let each
His adamantine coat gird well, and each
Fit well his helm, gripe fast his orbèd shield,
Borne ev'n or high; for this day will pour down,
If I conjecture aught, no drizzling show'r,
But rattling storm of arrows barbed with fire.'

JOHN MILTON *Paradise Lost*

# BIRTHDAYS

## January

## February

## March

## April

## May

## June

# BIRTHDAYS

## July

## August

## September

## October

## November

## December

I sat with Love upon a woodside well,
Leaning across the water, I and he;

DANTE GABRIEL ROSSETTI *Willow-Wood*

# Year Planner

## January

1
2
3
4
5
6
7
8
9
10
11
12
13
14
15
16
17
18
19
20
21
22
23
24
25
26
27
28
29
30
31

## February

1
2
3
4
5
6
7
8
9
10
11
12
13
14
15
16
17
18
19
20
21
22
23
24
25
26
27
28
29

## March

1
2
3
4
5
6
7
8
9
10
11
12
13
14
15
16
17
18
19
20
21
22
23
24
25
26
27
28
29
30
31

## April

1
2
3
4
5
6
7
8
9
10
11
12
13
14
15
16
17
18
19
20
21
22
23
24
25
26
27
28
29
30

## May

1
2
3
4
5
6
7
8
9
10
11
12
13
14
15
16
17
18
19
20
21
22
23
24
25
26
27
28
29
30
31

## June

1
2
3
4
5
6
7
8
9
10
11
12
13
14
15
16
17
18
19
20
21
22
23
24
25
26
27
28
29
30

# Year Planner

## July

1
2
3
4
5
6
7
8
9
10
11
12
13
14
15
16
17
18
19
20
21
22
23
24
25
26
27
28
29
30
31

## August

1
2
3
4
5
6
7
8
9
10
11
12
13
14
15
16
17
18
19
20
21
22
23
24
25
26
27
28
29
30
31

## September

1
2
3
4
5
6
7
8
9
10
11
12
13
14
15
16
17
18
19
20
21
22
23
24
25
26
27
28
29
30

## October

1
2
3
4
5
6
7
8
9
10
11
12
13
14
15
16
17
18
19
20
21
22
23
24
25
26
27
28
29
30
31

## November

1
2
3
4
5
6
7
8
9
10
11
12
13
14
15
16
17
18
19
20
21
22
23
24
25
26
27
28
29
30

## December

1
2
3
4
5
6
7
8
9
10
11
12
13
14
15
16
17
18
19
20
21
22
23
24
25
26
27
28
29
30
31

I sat with Love upon a woodside well,
   Leaning across the water, I and he;
   Now ever did he speak or look at me,
But touched his lute wherein was audible
The certain secret thing he had to tell:
   Only our mirrored eyes met silently
   In the low wave; and that sound came to be
The passionate voice I knew; and my tears fell.

And at their fall, his eyes beneath grew hers;
And with his foot and with his wing-feathers
   He swept the spring that watered my heart's drouth.
Then the dark ripples spread to the waving hair,
And as I stooped, her own lips rising there
   Bubbled with brimming kisses at my mouth.

DANTE GABRIEL ROSSETTI *Willow-Wood*

# *Acknowledgements*

The following pictures are reproduced with the kind permission of the Bridgeman Art Library, London:

Front Jacket: *Angels, from the Side Walls in the Chapel* by Benozzo Gozzoli (c1420–97) Plazzo Medici-Riccardi, Florence. p2 *Angel* by Abbott Handerson Thayer (1849–1921) National Museum of American Art, Smithsonian Inst. p 6 (detail) p14 (detail) from Ms 209 f.24v The Vintage: angel with sickle ordered by angel to cut vine, Lambeth Apocalypse (c1260) Lambeth Palace Library. p7 *The Guardian Angel* by Joshua Hargrave Sams Mann (fl. 1849–85) Haynes Fine Art at the Bindery Galleries, Broadway. p11 *Study for Homer's Apotheosis* by Jean-Auguste Dominque Ingres (1780–1867) Musee Bonnat, Bayonne. p15 *Dream of St Ursula* by Vittore arpaccio (c1460/1523/6) Galleria dell'Academia, Venice. p18 Untitled; *A woman adrift in a boat guided by Guradian Angels* by Anonymous, Forbes Magazine Collection/London. p19 *Christ in the Sepulchre, Guarded by Angels* by William Blake (1757–1827) Victoria and Albert Museum, London. p22 *Angel* (fresco) by Bernardino Luini (1480–1532) Pinacotea di Brera, Milan. p23 *Triumph of the Hapsburgs* by Luca Giordano (1632–1705) Monasteio de El Escorial, Spain. p26 *Annunciation* by Filippino Lippi (c1457/8–1504) Galleria dell'Accademia, Florence. p27 *The Annunciation,* Panel from the Main Altarpiece in Palencia Cathedral by Juan de Flandres (fl 1496–c1519) Castilla Leon, Palencia/Index. p30 *Cherubs, from the Adoration of the Shepherds* by Philippe de Champaigne (1604–74) Wallace Collection, London. p31 (top) *Amorini* (red chalk) by Francois Buucher (1703–70) (follower of) Wallace Collection, London. p31 (bottom) *Nativity* by Charles Poerson (1609–67) Louvre, Paris/Giraudon. p34/35 Christ, St John and two angels by Peter Paul Rubens (1577–1640) Collection of the Earl of Pembroke, Wilton House. p38 Ms65/1284 f.64v Fall of the rebel angels Tres Riches Heures du Duc de Berry (early 15th c) Musee Conde, Chantilly. p39 *The Fall of the Rebel Angels* by Sebastiano Ricci (1658–1734) Dulwich Picture Gallery, London. p42 *Angel with a Sword* (oak panel) by Hans Memling (fl 1465-d 1495) Wallace Collection, London. p43 Detail of Angles from the Altarpiece of St Barnabas by Sandro Botticelli (1444/5–1510) Galleria degli Uffizi, Florence. p46 *St Michael and the Devil* by Raffaello Sanzio Raphael of Urbino (1483–1520) Louvre, Paris/Giraudon. p47 (top, detail) *Tobias and the Archangel Raphael* by Francesco Botticini (c1446–97) Sacristy of Florence Cathedral. p47 (bottom) Ms 209 f35 Angel drags chained dragon away to prison, Lambeth Apocalypse (c1260) Lambeth Palace Library, London. p50 *Concert of Angels*, detail from the Isenheim Altarpiece by Mattias Grunewald (1455–1528) Unterlinden Museium, Colmar, France. p51 *Fall of Satan and the Rebel Angels from Heaven* by Jakob Swaneburgh (1571–1638) Rafael Vall Gallery, London. p54 *The Ascension of Christ* (fresco) by Jacopo Tintoretto (1518–94) Scola Grande di San Rocco, Venice. p58 *Benedicite No 1 'O all ye green things upon earth', 1899* by Edward A fellowes Prynne (1854–1921) Russell-Cotes Art Gallery and Museum, Bournemouth. p59 The Ramparts of God's House by John Melhuish Struwick (1849–1937) Christie's, London. Back Jacket:
Slipcase: (front) *Angel* by Abbott Handerson Thayer (1849–98) National Museum of American Art, Smithsonian Inst; (back)